Please check for separate

PIANO PART

on issue and return

CHRISTOPHER NORTON

the microjazz
flute collection *1*

easy pieces in popular styles for flute and piano

BOOSEY & HAWKES

london • new york • berlin • sydney

COMPOSER'S NOTE

This book, based on the **Microjazz** concept of graded pieces in popular styles, contains a set of rhythmically orientated compositions which take into account the range and particular character of the solo instrument.

Stimulating accompaniments allied to tuneful and rhythmic solo parts provide a storehouse of styles for players of all ages. Don't take the pieces too fast, be alert to the nuances of dynamic and articulation, and scrupulous about the rhythms. The solo parts are of moderate technical difficulty, but they all repay close study by players of any standard. Most of the accompaniments, which are also easy, may be played on piano, electric or electronic keyboards.

NOTE DU COMPOSITEUR

Ce livre est fondé sur le principe des **Microjazz**, une série de morceaux de style populaire classés par niveau de difficulté croissante. Il contient une sélection de pièces d'un grand intérêt rythmique qui tiennent compte des possibilités et du caractère propre de l'instrument soliste.

Des accompagnements qui encouragent la créativité, associés à des parties solistes mélodieuses et rythméesoffrent aux musiciens de tout âge une véritable mine de styles. Ne jouez pas ces morceaux trop vite, faites bien attention aux nuances et à l'articulation et soyez scrupuleusement exact en ce qui concerne le rythme. Les parties solistes sont d'une difficulté technique modérée, mais elles méritent une étude approfondie de la part de musiciens de tous niveaux. La plupart des accompagnements, qui sont également faciles, conviennent au piano, aussi bien qu'aux claviers électriques ou électroniques.

ANMERKUNG DES KOMPONISTEN

Die vorliegende Ausgabe folgt dem Prinzip der **Microjazz**-Reihe: Stücke in modernen Stilarten anzubieten, die nach Schwierigkeitsgraden geordnet sind. Das Heft enthält eine Sammlung rhythmische orientierter Kompositionen, die auf den besonderen Charakter und den Tonumfang des Soloinstruments Rücksicht nehmen.

Die spritzigen Begleitstimmen bieten zusammen mit den melodienreichen und rhythmischen Soloparts einen Fundus an Stilen für Spieler aller Altersstufen. Die Stücke sollten nicht zu schnell gespielt werden, und die nuancen der Dynamik und Artikulation sollten ebenso präzise beachtet werden wie die rhythmische Genauigkeit. Die Soloparts sind mittelschwer, aber eine eingehende Beschäftigung mit ihnen lohnt sich für Spieler aller Stufen. Die meisten Begleitstimmen, die auch leicht zu bewältigen sind, können auf dem Klavier oder auf elektronischen Tasteninstrumenten gespielt werden.

作曲者註

本書はポピュラー様式による漸進的小品集である**マイクロジャズ**の概念に基づいており、ソロ楽器の音域や、とりわけその性格を考慮した、リズム的適応性を備えた作品集である。

興奮を呼び起こす伴奏、同時に音楽的でリズミカルなソロ・パートが、すべての年齢層の演奏者に様式の宝庫を提供する。演奏に際しては、急ぎすぎぬこと、またディナミークとアーティキュレーションのニュアンスにも注意をはらい、正確なリズムを守ること。ソロ・パートの技巧的難易度は中庸であるが、これらはみな、いかなる水準の奏者の練習にも報いられるものである。やさしいものも含めて、そのほとんどの伴奏はピアノもしくは電気及び電子鍵盤楽器により演奏できるものである。

クリストファー・ノートン

Contents

Cover design by Electric Echo
Music setting by Andrew Jones

1. Challenging Times

Flute

Christopher Norton

2. Footsteps

Christopher Norton

3. Seesaw

Christopher Norton

4. Banana Tree

Christopher Norton

5. Cruise Liner

Christopher Norton

6. What's the Score?

Christopher Norton

7. Softly does it

Christopher Norton

8. Walking Tour

Christopher Norton

9. A Stroll

Christopher Norton

10. Venezuelan Holiday

Christopher Norton

11. Little Lamb

Christopher Norton

12. Mango Juice

Christopher Norton

13. Fine Views

Christopher Norton

14. Glad to be Back

Christopher Norton

15. Break Time

Christopher Norton

16. A Walk by the Sea

Christopher Norton

17. Ramblers

Christopher Norton

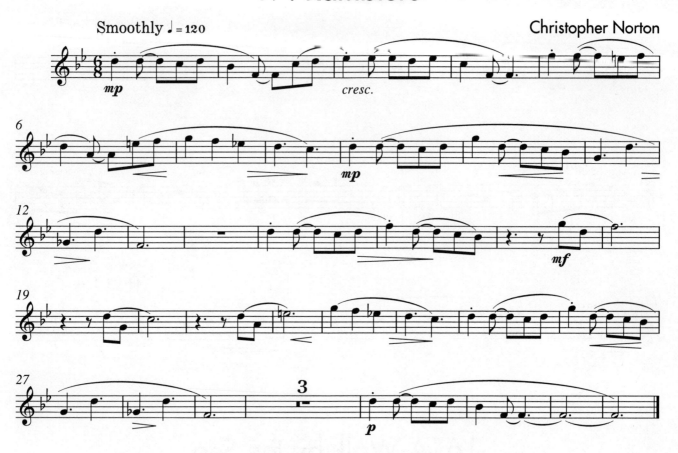

18. Cheery Again

Christopher Norton

19. Seashore

Christopher Norton

20. Jaunty

Christopher Norton

Printed by
Halstan & Co. Ltd., Amersham, Bucks., England

CHRISTOPHER NORTON

the microjazz
flute collection *1*

easy pieces in popular styles for flute and piano

PIANO ACCOMPANIMENTS

BOOSEY & HAWKES

london • new york • berlin • sydney

Contents

1. Challenging Times

Christopher Norton

2. Footsteps

Christopher Norton

3. Seesaw

Christopher Norton

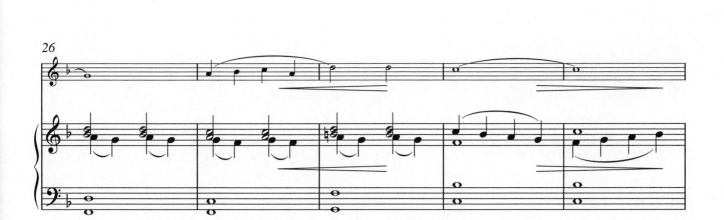

4. Banana Tree

Christopher Norton

5. Cruise Liner

Christopher Norton

6. What's the Score?

Christopher Norton

7. Softly does it

Christopher Norton

8. Walking Tour

Christopher Norton

D.C. al Fine

9. A Stroll

Christopher Norton

10. Venezuelan Holiday

Christopher Norton

11. Little Lamb

Christopher Norton

12. Mango Juice

Christopher Norton

13. Fine Views

Christopher Norton

14. Glad to be Back

Christopher Norton

15. Break Time

Christopher Norton

16. A Walk by the Sea

Christopher Norton

17. Ramblers

Christopher Norton

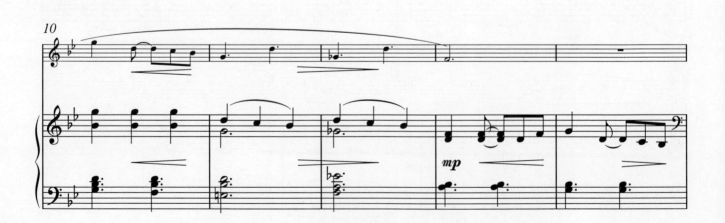

18. Cheery Again

Christopher Norton

19. Seashore

Christopher Norton

20. Jaunty

Christopher Norton

Printed by
Halstan & Co. Ltd., Amersham, Bucks., England